The
Classical Organ
Book I

Edited by Stephen Duro

WISE PUBLICATIONS
London/New York/Paris/Sydney/Copenhagen/Madrid

Exclusive Distributors:
MUSIC SALES LIMITED
8/9 Frith Street, London W1V 5TZ, England.
MUSIC SALES PTY LIMITED
120 Rothschild Avenue, Rosebery, NSW 2018, Australia.
MUSIC SALES CORPORATION
257 Park Avenue South, New York, NY10010, United States of America.

Order No. AM92621
ISBN 0-7119-4698-1
This book © Copyright 1995 by Wise Publications

Music edited by Stephen Duro
Music processed by Enigma Music Production Services

Book design by Pearce Marchbank, Studio Twenty
Cover photograph by Pearce Marchbank
Quarked by Ben May

Printed in the United Kingdom by
Caligraving Limited, Thetford, Norfolk.

YOUR GUARANTEE OF QUALITY
As publishers, we strive to produce every book to the highest commercial standards.
The music has been freshly engraved and the book has been carefully designed to
minimise awkward page turns and to make playing from it a real pleasure.
Particular care has been given to specifying acid-free, neutral-sized paper made from
pulps which have not been elemental chlorine bleached. This pulp is from farmed
sustainable forests and was produced with special regard for the environment.
Throughout, the printing and binding have been planned to ensure a sturdy,
attractive publication which should give years of enjoyment.
If your copy fails to meet our high standards,
please inform us and we will gladly replace it.

Music Sales' complete catalogue describes thousands of titles and is
available in full colour sections by subject, direct from Music Sales Limited.
Please state your areas of interest and send a cheque/postal order
for £1.50 for postage to:
Music Sales Limited, Newmarket Road,
Bury St. Edmunds, Suffolk IP33 3YB.

Andante Cantabile

from Quartet in D, Op.11

PETER ILYICH TCHAIKOVSKY
(1840-1893)

Andante in F

LUDWIG VAN BEETHOVEN
(1770-1827)

Andante grazioso

Ave Maria

Johann Sebastian Bach (1685-1750)
Charles Gounod (1818-1893)

Ave Verum Corpus

Wolfgang Amadeus Mozart
(1756-1791)

Andante con pieta

Alleluja

WOLFGANG AMADEUS MOZART
(1756-1791)

16

Chorale
Op.68, No.4

ROBERT SCHUMANN
(1810-1856)

Bourrée

from French Overture in B Minor

Johann Sebastian Bach
(1685-1750)

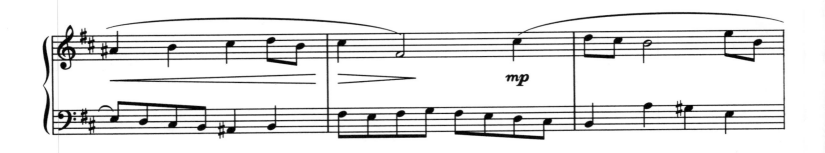

Bridal March

from 'Lohengrin'

RICHARD WAGNER
(1813-1883)

Moderato con moto

Jesu, Joy of Man's Desiring

Chorale from Church Cantata No. 147

JOHANN SEBASTIAN BACH
(1685-1750)

Largo

from 'Xerxes'

GEORG FRIDERIC HANDEL
(1685-1759)

Austrian Hymn

JOSEPH HAYDN
(1732-1809)

Cradle Song

FRANZ SCHUBERT
(1797-1828)

March

from 'Scipio'

Georg Frideric Handel
(1685-1759)

O For The Wings Of A Dove

from 'Hear My Prayer'

Felix Mendelssohn-Bartholdy
(1809-1847)

March

from 'Egmont'

LUDWIG VAN BEETHOVEN
(1770-1827)

D.C. al Fine

Lullaby

EDVARD GRIEG
(1843-1907)

Melody in F

ANTON RUBINSTEIN
(1829-1894)

O Sacred Head Now Wounded

Chorale

JOHANN SEBASTIAN BACH
(1685-1750)

Pilgrims' Chorus

from 'Tannhäuser'

RICHARD WAGNER
(1813-1883)

Romance

from Eine Kleine Nachtmusik

WOLFGANG AMADEUS MOZART
(1756-1791)

Andante

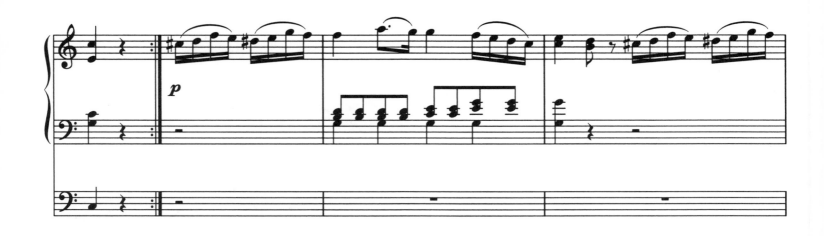

A Stronghold Sure

Chorale

MARTIN LUTHER
(1483-1546)

Pastoral Symphony

from 'Messiah'

GEORG FRIDERIC HANDEL
(1685-1759)

Larghetto